Number Five

Dorling Kinderlsey
www.dk.com

Editor Fiona Munro
Designer Lisa Hollis

Published in Great Britain in 1997
by Dorling Kindersley Limited, 9 Henrietta St, London WC2E 8PS
This edition published in 2000

A CIP catalogue record for this book is available from the British Library.

ISBN 0-7513-6705-2

Color reproduction by DOT Gradations
Printed in Hong Kong by Wing King Tong

Number Five

COLIN AND JACQUI HAWKINS

Dorling Kindersley

"I'm the best of all
the Numberlies,"
said Number Five.

She lived in the fifth house in Numbertown.
It was a smart house with five pink
chimney-pots and five orange windows.
The address was 5, Number Lane.

Every morning, Number Five went for a five mile run, then raced home for a big breakfast of five beefburgers with lots and lots of ketchup.

"All that running has made me hungry," said Number Five.

"YUMMY! YUMMY!"

she munched.
"My burgers are best."

And five minutes later they were all gone.

After breakfast, Number Five brushed
her teeth for five minutes.
She used five toothbrushes and
five tubes of toothpaste,
which made her teeth five times shinier.

"I like my teeth sparkling clean,"
said Number Five.
"They are the whitest and best teeth
in Numbertown," she grinned.

She was good at lots of different sports. She had won five certificates, five rosettes and five shields. But so far, Number Five had won only four cups. She was determined to win another to make it five.

I'm the best!

"I'm the best,
I'll beat the rest!"

One sunny day, Number Five was out for a five mile walk when she saw a large poster on the park railings. It said,

Numbertown Big Race. All welcome.
Win the Numbertown Cup.

"I'm going to win that cup," boasted Number Five.

"I'm the best,
I'll beat the rest!"

All the Numberlies trained very hard and at last, the big day came. The Numberlies lined up for the start of the race.

Ready . . . steady . . . go!

They were off! Number Five raced away and went straight into the lead.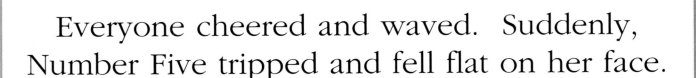

"I'm the best, I'll beat the rest!"

she puffed.

Everyone cheered and waved. Suddenly, Number Five tripped and fell flat on her face.

Number One whizzed by and raced
towards the finishing line.

"I'm first!" he shouted.
"I've won the cup!" Everyone clapped.
Poor Number Five limped in last.
"It isn't fair," she cried.
"**I'm** the best runner in Numbertown."
"Ha! Ha!" laughed Number Two.
"You're not the best runner,
but you **are** the worst loser!"

Number Five was very upset.
"I know. I'll go fishing.
It will cheer me up," she said.

She was soon sitting in the sunshine
on the riverbank.
"Have you caught anything?" said a voice.
It was nosey Number Four.
"No, not yet," replied Number Five.
"Hee! Hee!" laughed Number Four.
"You couldn't catch a flea!"

SPLASH!

Number Four laughed so much,
he toppled into the river.

"Help!" he yelled, "I can't swim!"
"Don't panic," shouted Number Five.
"Catch hold of my line and hang on."
And in five ticks she had fished a very
wet Number Four out of the river.

The next day, all the Numberlies met to celebrate Number Four's rescue.

They all cheered as Number Five was given a big, gold cup for bravery.

"Hooray!" "Hooray!" "Hooray!" "Hooray!" "Hooray!"

Number Five was proud of her fifth cup! All the Numberlies cheered,

"When put to the test, you **are** the best!"